Games for 1, 2 or More

CP CHILDRENS PRESS, CHICAGO

Art Director
Thomas Petiet, M.F.A.

Senior Editors
Mary Rush M.F.A.
Sharon Irvine, B.A.

Contributors
Nancy Muhlbach, M.A.
Jerry Gillmore, B.A.
Mary White, B.A.
Edith Wolter, B.S.
Susan Keezer
Barbara Daniel
Virginia Foster, A.B.

Readability Consultants
Donald E.P. Smith, Ph.D.
School of Education
University of Michigan

Judith K. Smith, Ph.D.
University of Michigan

Instructional Development Consultant
Joel B. Fleming, M.A.
Instructional Development & Technology
Michigan State University

Synectics Consultant
Gershom Clark Morningstar, M.A.
President, Wolverine-Morningstar Media

Crafts Consultant
Laurie A. Flynn, B.A.
Little Seville Gallery, Pensacola, Fla.

Library Consultant
Noel Winkler, M.A.L.S.
Lecturer, Children's Literature
Elementary Librarian, Media Center
School of Education
University of Michigan

Contents

Challenge yourself . . . challenge your friends. Play Burmese hop-scotch or the Indian Bowl Game. Test your strength and skill in your homemade gymnasium. Exercise your mind with fascinating memory games and guessing games.

All these game ideas, and many more, are in this book. Games are fun. They are rewarding. Play alone or with your friends. Either way you'll have fun.

You don't need expensive equipment or money for these games. Most of them use things you already have. Others ask you to make your equipment from things that you can easily find around the house, such as milk cartons, paper plates, string.

These games are fascinating. The pictures help you see how each game is played. Teach a new game to your brothers or sisters. Challenge your parents or your teacher to a game of skill. Make up your own game. Remember, somebody invented baseball!

Here are a few hints that make game-playing safer and more enjoyable.

- Read the instructions carefully.
- Make or get everything you need before you start playing.
- Be a good sport. Be sure the other players know and understand the rules *before* you start competing.
- Be CAREFUL. Don't be careless and hurt yourself or someone else.
- Don't make a mess. Clean up after yourself.

Enjoy yourself. Games help you keep your body strong and healthy. Learn how to run, throw, catch and exercise the right way. As you get better and better, you will become stronger and more sure of yourself.

ALONE

OR ALMOST ALONE

Indian Bowl Game

KEEP six peach, plum or prune pits.

DRAW a stripe halfway around each pit with a felt pen or paint.

FIND a big bowl like a salad bowl.

PUT the pits in the bowl and toss them in the air. See how many you can catch in the bowl with the striped side up.

TOSS the pits in the air and catch them ten times.

PLAY this game with your friends and keep score. Count one point for each pit that lands with the striped side showing.

FIND out if the North American Indians who lived in your area played this game. Most tribes in the country played one like it.

Five Small Stones

FIND five small, flat stones.

SIT on the ground and toss one stone in the air. Try to catch it on the back of your hand.

TOSS two stones in the air and catch them on the back of your hand.

ADD one more stone after each good catch until you can catch all five stones.

PLAY this game with your friends as the children in Korea do. Start with one stone each time and add another only after a good catch.

PASS the stones to the next player for his turn if you miss a catch.

Spool Racer

FIND an empty thread spool, a rubber band, two small nails and a bobby pin.

GET a large bead and a piece of 1/4 inch dowel that is three inches long. If you don't have a dowel, cut a 3 inch section from an old pencil.

POUND the nails most of the way into the spool on both sides of one hole.

PUT one end of the rubber band in the U part of a bobby pin. Drop it between the nails into the hole in the spool.

WRAP the other end of the rubber band around the nails.

PUSH the bobby pin and rubber band through the hole in the bead.

TAKE out the bobby pin and push the dowel through the loop in the rubber band where it comes through the bead.

TURN the dowel around and around to twist the rubber band tight.

PUT the racer on a smooth surface and see how fast it will go.

Tiddly-Button Golf

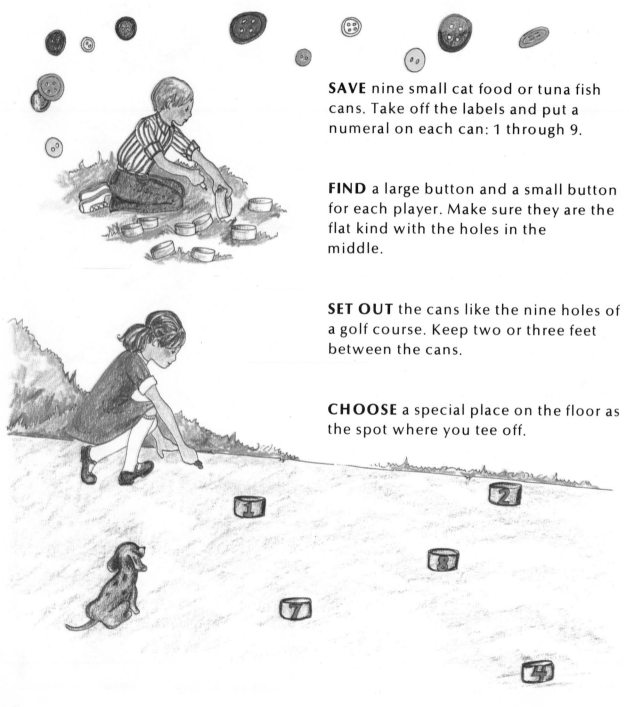

SAVE nine small cat food or tuna fish cans. Take off the labels and put a numeral on each can: 1 through 9.

FIND a large button and a small button for each player. Make sure they are the flat kind with the holes in the middle.

SET OUT the cans like the nine holes of a golf course. Keep two or three feet between the cans.

CHOOSE a special place on the floor as the spot where you tee off.

TRY to shoot the small button into the cans by pressing on the edge of it with the larger button.

START from the tee off spot and shoot for can number 1. After you get the button in this can, take it out, put it next to the can, and shoot for can number 2.

COUNT one point for each shot it takes to get the button in a can. The player with the lowest score after nine holes is the winner.

Pick Up Sticks

TRY this game that Vietnamese children play with chopsticks.

USE chopsticks if you have them. If not, save ten popsicle sticks. Then find a small ball that will bounce.

LAY the popsicle sticks on the floor in a straight line.

THROW the ball in the air and pick up one stick. Catch the ball in the same hand after you let it bounce once.

KEEP this stick in your hand and pick up another the same way. Make sure the ball doesn't bounce more than one time.

TRY to pick up one more stick each time until you can get all ten at once.

Penning the Pigs

KEEP the top from a shoe box or find another kind of box lid with low sides.

ASK your mother for the top from a small size oatmeal or cornmeal box.

CUT AWAY about two inches from the rim of the round top. Then cut out the circle from the center, about 1/4 inch from the edge.

GLUE the rim that is left upside down on the inside of the shoe box lid.

PUT three marbles into the shoe box lid. Try to catch them in the pen you made from the round lid.

TIME yourself to see how long it takes you to pen all three "pigs." The first two pigs will try to sneak out of the pen just as you almost have the third one penned.

Handkerchief Kick

FIND a large man's handkerchief or a rag that is about the same size.

TIE a big knot in the middle of it. You may have to tie two or three knots in the same place.

KICK the handkerchief up in the air with the side of your foot.

TRY to kick it again with the other foot before it touches the ground.

FIND some friends and play it as Korean children do. Kick the handkerchief back and forth without using your hands.

DROP OUT of the game if you miss. Play this way until only one person is left.

Whammy Whizzer

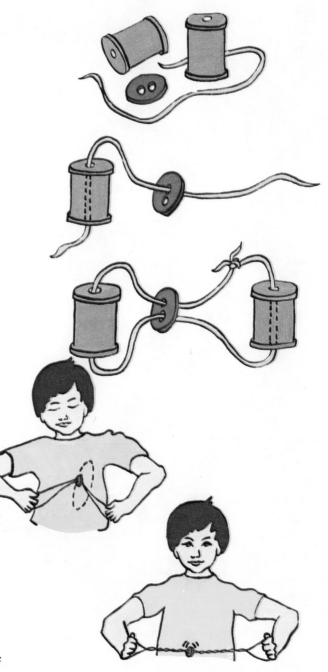

FIND a large button with two holes in the middle and two empty thread spools.

GET a piece of string that is about 28 inches long.

THREAD the string through one hole in the button and the hole in the middle of the spool.

BRING the string around to go through the other hole in the button and the middle of the other spool.

TIE the ends of the string together.

HOLD a spool in each hand and twirl the button around and around to twist the string tight.

PULL the spools hard and listen. See if you can change the sound with a larger or smaller button.

FRiSBee

MAKE your own frisbee by gluing or stapling two paper plates together with the fronts touching. Or use an aluminum or aluminum foil pie plate.

TOSS the frisbee from the side of your hand or try your own methods.

INVITE your dog to play with you if he will bring the frisbee back.

FIND a wastebasket or a clothes basket and lay it on its side to use as a target. See if you can throw your frisbee into it.

USE an old tire as a target. Hang it from a tree limb with a rope.

TRY to toss the frisbee through the center of the tire.

CALL a friend and have contests with him. Maybe he has a dog that can play.

Hopscotch International

Landing in Paradise

DRAW the plan as children in Norway do.

START with square 1 and move to square 8 by hopping through the numbers on your *right* foot.

LAND in Paradise on both feet. Hop back from 8 to 1 on your *left* foot.

Burmese Hopscotch

USE any kind of plan but always hop with both feet. In order to move, you must start in a squatting position and always land the same way.

Hopscotch in Vietnam

HOP with another person, one foot at a time. If either player jumps on a line give another couple a turn.

Red Light-Green Light

TRY JUMPING from square to square with your eyes closed as children in the Soviet Union do. The watchers will yell "Red Light" if you land on a line.

STOP and give someone else a turn if you hear this. "Green Light" means you may keep going until you miss.

Your Own Thing

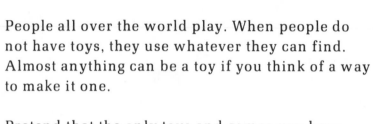

People all over the world play. When people do not have toys, they use whatever they can find. Almost anything can be a toy if you think of a way to make it one.

Pretend that the only toys and games you have are the things you find all around you.

Think what you can do with an empty egg carton or those little trays that meat and tomatoes come in. How can you use an old milk carton? How about some little boxes no one wants any more?

Look around your yard or along the sides of your street. What great ways can you think of to use some small stones or odd pieces of wood and wire?

Maybe some small sticks will be useful; or an old tire the man at the service station doesn't want anymore. Games and toys don't have to come from the store. Sometimes they are all around you.

PHYSICAL FEATS

Rooster Fight

MAKE a circle about six feet across.

STAND in the circle with a friend.

PUT your right hand behind your back and grasp your left ankle. Now grip your right arm with your left hand behind your back. Both of you must keep your hands in this position throughout the fight.

HOP toward your friend. Try to push each other out of the circle. If one of you lets go of a foot or an arm, or steps outside of the circle, he loses.

Chicken Fight

MARK a circle about ten feet across.

HAVE each player squat and grab his ankles. Keep this position throughout the contest.

USE only shoulders and backs (no hands) to try to knock each other over or out of the circle.

WATCH the fun. The last one to remain squatting is the winner.

Raise the Water

HAVE two friends hold the ends of a rope.

LINE up the other players.

BEGIN with the rope lying flat on the ground.

HAVE everyone jump over it. Raise it a little higher. Keep it loose so no one will trip over it.

RAISE it higher each time everyone has tried to jump over it. The higher the rope is, the fewer the number of players who will be able to jump over it.

KEEP RAISING and jumping. The one who jumps the highest is the winner.

Chinese Get Up

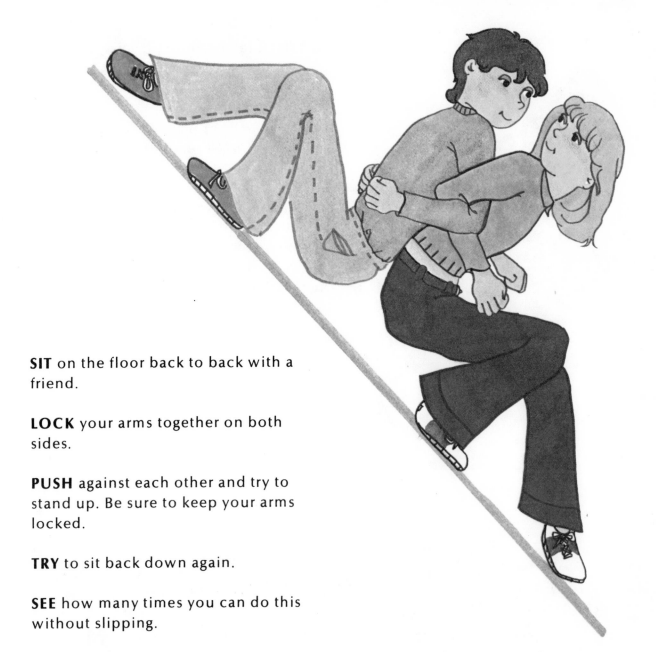

SIT on the floor back to back with a friend.

LOCK your arms together on both sides.

PUSH against each other and try to stand up. Be sure to keep your arms locked.

TRY to sit back down again.

SEE how many times you can do this without slipping.

Tug of War

GATHER ten or more players. Divide them into two equal teams. Draw a line across a field or floor.

LINE the teams up single file, one team facing the other on either side of the line.

HAVE each player take hold of the waist of the player in front of him. The head person on each team grasps the waist of the head person of the other team facing him across the center line.

GIVE a signal. Each team tries to pull all of the opposing team over the line. The team that does, wins.

TRY playing this, only instead of holding on to each other's waist, the members of both teams grip the same rope and try to pull all of the opposing team across the center line.

Tractor

CHOOSE a soft grassy spot outdoors or a carpeted area inside. Clear the area of any objects.

FACE two players in opposite directions on their hands and knees. They must be so close their feet almost touch. These are the "tractors." Two other players are "drivers."

SIT the drivers facing each other on the tractors so they hold on with their legs around their tractor's waist.

GIVE a signal and each driver stretches his arms in front of him and tries to grab the hands of the other driver and pull him off his tractor. The driver who stays on his tractor wins. It's a tie if both are pulled off at the same time.

CHANGE PLACES with drivers and tractors after each match.

Tug for Two

GET ten yards of heavy string or twine.

WRAP it around your hand thirty times.

SLIP the twine off of your hand and divide it into two equal rings. Keep them joined in the middle. Be careful not to unwind the twine.

START to wrap the extra twine around the center where the two loops join. Wrap it around the two loops also. Use any twine left to make the center stronger. Finish with a few strong knots.

MARK a center line on the floor or on the ground.

HOLD one side of the tug grip. Have a friend hold the other side. The center line should be between you.

PULL until one of you is pulled over the line or loses his grip.

Weight Lifting

FIND two empty half gallon plastic bottles with handles. Fill them with an equal amount of sand or gravel.

HOLD one bottle in each hand.

STRETCH your arms out shoulder high on each side. Keep your arms stiff.

SEE how long you can hold them in that position.

RAISE and lower the weights as many times as you can.

STRETCH them in front of you and swing them up to your head and down to your sides.

SWING them in front of you crossing and uncrossing your arms.

PUT more sand in the bottles to make it more difficult.

THINK of other feats to perform with your weights. Challenge a friend to a contest.

Broomstick Gym

SAW off the broom end of an old broom.

SMOOTH the rough edges with sandpaper.

GET a 3/4 inch dowel rod, three feet long if you can't find an old broom.

USE this stick for the Physical Feats that follow.

Rocking Horse

LIE on your stomach on the floor.

BEND your knees so your heels are over your bottom.

HOLD the stick on the front of your feet.

PULL with your arms then push against the stick with your feet.

KEEP doing this and you will rock back and forth.

BRING your chest and thighs off the floor as high as you can each time.

Broomstick Balance

MAKE a bridge by laying a broomstick through the backs of two chairs that are a little way apart.

SEAT yourself on the broomstick. Cross your legs and extend them out straight in front of you.

USE a stick or cane to help you get balanced, then put the stick down.

SEE how long you can stay balanced without using the stick to help you.

Stick Pull

SIT on the floor with a friend. Put the soles of your feet against the soles of his feet.

GRASP a stick and hold it crosswise above your toes. The friend grips the stick, too.

TRY TO PULL each other to a standing position. The one who is pulled over, or the one who lets go of the stick, loses.

Your Own Thing

Most physical feats test your strength and skill. Can you run faster than your friend? Can he beat you at Indian wrestling?

Learn the right way to run, throw, catch, and exercise. Practice a lot. Try to do a little more each time. At first it will seem hard but as you do these things the right way over and over, you will get better. Then it becomes fun!

Try things that seem hard for you. This is how you learn and grow. When ever you try to throw farther, run faster, climb higher, lift more, or see how long you can do something, you become stronger and more sure of yourself.

QUIET GAMES

Numbers Racket

CHOOSE a leader.

DIVIDE the other players into two even teams.

GIVE each player a four by six inch card with a number from one to ten written on it. The players on one team have the same numbers as the players on the other.

HAVE the leader call out a number between one and twenty-five.

TRY to be the first team to send up players with cards that add up to the called number. If you do, you get a point.

TAKE AWAY two points for a wrong answer.

Dark Dog

GIVE a blindfold, pencil and paper to everyone.

HAVE everybody sit down and put on a blindfold securely. No peeking.

ASK one person to be the "guide." He will call directions for the others to follow. "Draw the head of a dog. Now draw his feet, body, tail, tongue, ears, collar, spots, and so on . . ."

TAKE OFF the blindfolds after the "guide" has finished giving drawing instructions.

SHOW each other the dogs that were drawn in the dark.

HAVE lots of fun drawing different things while you are blindfolded.

Direct & Draw

FIND one or more friends to play this with you.

GIVE each one a pencil and paper.

ARRANGE everybody so no one can see the other's papers.

CHOOSE a "Director." The others will be followers. The Director's job is to think of something for the followers to draw. He won't tell them what it is. He must give such clear instructions that the follower's finished drawings will be almost the same as what the director draws.

LISTEN as the Director tells you step by step what he is drawing.

FOLLOW his directions carefully.

TRY to draw each step on your own paper as he tells you.

SHOW each other your finished drawings. The clearer the directions the more alike the picture will be.

Parson's Cat

HAVE a group of people sit in a circle.

START by having one person say, "The Parson's cat is . . . angry." (Any word beginning with *A*.) The next person will say, "The Parson's cat is angry and beautiful." (Any word beginning with *B*.)

PROCEED around the circle with the next person always repeating all of the words describing the Parson's cat and adding another that begins with the next letter in the alphabet.

CONTINUE until you have used all of the letters of the alphabet. If someone forgets some of the words or cannot think of a word for the next turn, he is out of the game.

PLAY this as the English children do. Perhaps you could make up your own game of "Packing a rocket to go to the moon," using things beginning with each letter of the alphabet.

Grab & Guess

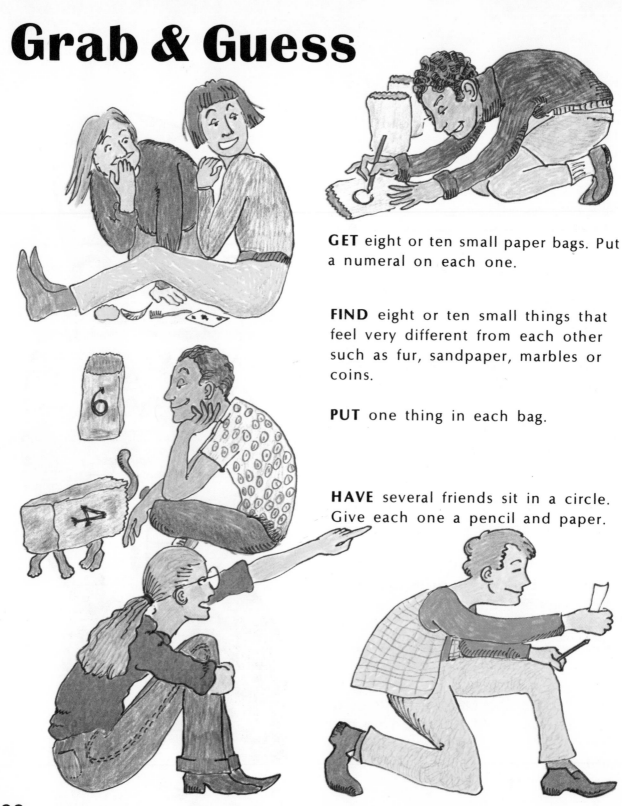

GET eight or ten small paper bags. Put a numeral on each one.

FIND eight or ten small things that feel very different from each other such as fur, sandpaper, marbles or coins.

PUT one thing in each bag.

HAVE several friends sit in a circle. Give each one a pencil and paper.

PASS a numbered bag to one friend. Tell him to put his hand in the bag and feel the object inside without peeking.

HAVE him write down the bag number and what he thinks is inside. Keep the guess secret.

PASS each bag around the circle until everyone has written down his guess. Check the list and see who guessed the most things correctly.

TRY it again with objects that are harder to guess.

Sniff It

GET ten small paper cups. Put a number on each.

HAVE an adult help you find different smelling stuff to put in each cup, such as vinegar, vanilla, cinnamon, garlic, and soap.

BLINDFOLD each player.

HAVE each player guess what he smells in each cup.

WRITE down the number and guess for each cup.

Drop It

HANG a sheet across a table or set up a cardboard box screen.

COLLECT ten or fifteen things that will not break when you drop them: aluminum pie tins, tissue paper and nails. They all should sound different when they are dropped.

DROP the things one at a time behind your screen. Wait a few seconds after each drop.

SEE if the listeners can guess what was dropped.

Egg Carton Kalah

GET a long egg carton. Put three dried beans in each of the twelve pits of the carton.

SIT on one side of the carton and have a friend sit on the other. The pit on each player's far right is his Kalah.

TAKE TURNS picking up all of the beans in any one of your own pits.

PUT them one by one in each following pit around to your right. If there are enough beans to go beyond your own Kalah, distribute them in your opponent's pits, skipping his Kalah. The beans you place in his pits now belong to him.

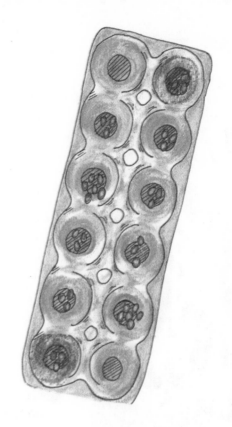

TAKE another turn if your last bean lands in your own Kalah. If the last bean lands in an empty pit on your own side, you capture all of your opponent's beans in the opposite pit and put them in your own Kalah along with the capturing bean.

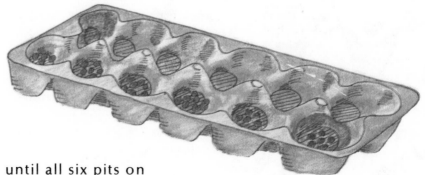

CONTINUE playing until all six pits on one side are empty. The player with all the beans wins.

Your Own Thing

Quiet games can be played almost any where—in small spaces or crowded places. You can play them alone, with a friend, or with a room full of friends. They are often "thought" games to excerise your mind or just to pass the time.

Paper and pencil are all you need for a lot of games. List things of the same kind, such as words that begin with "q" or things that are made of wood. See who can make the longest list. Or, take turns adding a line to a drawing or a letter to a word. What surprises you end up with!

Memory games are quiet games. In them you try to: remember and repeat what you heard, remember what you saw, or, remember and repeat what someone did.

Guessing games are good quiet games. Usually one person knows the answer and others try to guess what it is, or, a lot of people know the answer and only one person guesses.

A good quiet game would be to see who can make up the quietest game. S-h-h-h-h.

INDEX

ILLUSTRATORS

ALONE OR ALMOST ALONE

PHYSICAL FEATS

QUIET GAMES